Violin Exam Pieces

ABRSM Grade 2

Selected from the 2020–2023 syllabus

Name

Date c

Contents

Violin consultant: Kathy Blackwell
Footnotes: Anthony Burton

Other pieces for Grade 2   DUET *with violin accompaniment*   PF/VN *with piano or violin accompaniment*

LIST A

4   **J. S. Bach**   Musette, arr. Suzuki. *Suzuki Violin School, Vol. 2* (Alfred)

5   **Boismortier**   Rigaudon, arr. Mohrs (*upper part*). *Duets for Fun: Violins* (Schott)   DUET

6   **Finger**   Air, arr. Mohrs (*trill optional*). *My First Concert for Violin* (Schott)

7   **Haydn**   Minuet and Trio, arr. Nelson (*without DC*). *Piece by Piece 1 for Violin* (Boosey & Hawkes)

8   **G. B. Martini**   Gavotte, arr. de Keyser & Waterman. *The Best of Grade 2 Violin* (Faber) or *The Young Violinist's Repertoire, Book 1* (Faber)

9   **Trad. Irish**   Red-Haired Boy, arr. Huws Jones (*violin melody*). *The Fiddler Playalong Violin Collection 2* (Boosey & Hawkes) or *Jigs, Reels & Hornpipe* (Boosey & Hawkes)   PF/VN

10   **Trad. Scottish**   Soldier's Joy, arr. Nelson (*upper part*). *Tunes You Know 2 for Violin Duet* (Boosey & Hawkes)   DUET

LIST B

4   **Katherine & Hugh Colledge**   Weeping Willow: No. 10 from *Fast Forward for Violin* (Boosey & Hawkes)

5   **Edward Jones**   Glwysen, arr. Huws Jones (*violin melody*). *The Fiddler Playalong Violin Collection 2* (Boosey & Hawkes) or *The Celtic Fiddler* (Boosey & Hawkes)   PF/VN

6   **Mozart**   Theme (from *Sonata in A*, K. 331, 1st movt), arr. Gazda & Clark (*upper part; grace notes optional*). *Compatible Duets for Strings, Vol. 2: Violin* (Carl Fischer)   DUET

7   **Offenbach**   Barcarolle (from *The Tales of Hoffmann*), arr. Gregory (*with repeats*). *Vamoosh Violin, Book 2* (Vamoosh)

8   **Tchaikovsky**   Waltz (from *The Sleeping Beauty*), arr. Cohen. *Superpieces* (Faber) or *The Best of Grade 2 Violin* (Faber)

9   **Trad. North American**   Simple Gifts, arr. Waterfield & Beach. *The Best of Grade 2 Violin* (Faber) or *O Shenandoah! for Violin* (Faber)

10   **Trad.**   Greensleeves, arr. Nelson (*upper part*). *Tunes You Know 1 for Violin Duet* (Boosey & Hawkes)   DUET

LIST C

4   **Arlen & Harburg**   We're off to see the wizard (from *The Wizard of Oz*), arr. Davey, Hussey & Sebba. *Abracadabra Violin (Third Edition)* (Collins Music)   PF/VN

5   **Bartók**   Play Song: No. 9 from *44 Duos for Two Violins, Vol. 1* (*upper part*) (Universal)   DUET

6   **Kathy & David Blackwell**   Jacob's Dance. *Fiddle Time Sprinters* (OUP)   PF/VN

7   **Thomas Gregory**   Smooth Operator. *Vamoosh Violin, Book 2* (Vamoosh)

8   **Ferdinand Seitz**   Gypsy Dance (*ending at b. 47*). *Violin Recital Album, Vol. 2* (Bärenreiter)   PF/VN

9   **Trad.**   Jack Tar, arr. Huws Jones (*violin melody*). *The Seafaring Fiddler* (Boosey & Hawkes)   PF/VN

10   **Pam Wedgwood**   Siberian Galop. *The Best of Grade 2 Violin* (Faber) or *Up-Grade! Violin Grades 1–2* (Faber)

First published in 2019 by ABRSM (Publishing) Ltd,
a wholly owned subsidiary of ABRSM, 4 London Wall Place,
London EC2Y 5AU, United Kingdom
© 2019 by The Associated Board of the Royal Schools of Music
Distributed worldwide by Oxford University Press

Music origination by Julia Bovee
Cover by Kate Benjamin & Andy Potts, with thanks to Brighton College
Printed in England by Halstan & Co. Ltd, Amersham, Bucks.,
on materials from sustainable sources.

Allegretto

from Clarinet Quintet, K. 581, fourth movement

Arranged by Nicholas Scott-Burt

W. A. Mozart
(1756–91)

Towards the end of his short life, the Austrian composer Wolfgang Amadeus Mozart wrote two masterpieces for his friend Anton Stadler, one of the first virtuoso players of the clarinet. One was a concerto with orchestra; the other, written in September 1789, was a quintet with two violins, viola and cello. The last of the four movements of the quintet is a set of variations on a jaunty theme, which is arranged here for violin and piano.

Menuet in G

BWV Anh. II 114

A:2

Arranged by Edward Huws Jones

Christian Petzold
(1677–c.1733)

Johann Sebastian Bach presented two handwritten 'Little Keyboard Books' to his second wife Anna Magdalena. The first, from 1722, consisted entirely of his own music; the second, from 1725, was an anthology of pieces mostly by other composers, for Anna Magdalena to play for enjoyment or to teach to the couple's children. This 'Menuet', from the 1725 collection, was written by Christian Petzold, a German organist and composer at the court of Saxony in Dresden, which Bach visited several times. The minuet was a graceful dance of French origin which was popular throughout the 18th century.

© 2004 by The Associated Board of the Royal Schools of Music
Reproduced from *Violin Exam Pieces 2005–2007*, Grade 2 (ABRSM)

Minuett

No. 7 from *The Double Dealer*, Z. 592

Arranged by David Blackwell

Henry Purcell
(1659–95)

The English composer Henry Purcell wrote large quantities of music throughout his short life for the thriving London theatres. Many plays at the time included songs or longer vocal scenes, and most had instrumental music before each act. It was for the first production of William Congreve's comedy *The Double Dealer* at the Drury Lane theatre in late 1693 that Purcell composed this piece for a group of string players, in the French dance rhythm of the minuet. He seems to have been pleased with the result, because he also made an arrangement of it as an 'Air' for solo harpsichord.

Theme

from Symphony No. 1, third movement

B:1

Arranged by Peter Gritton

Gustav Mahler
(1860–1911)

The Austrian composer and conductor Gustav Mahler wrote ten symphonies, the last of which was left unfinished. The first, written in 1888, has a third movement which Mahler said was suggested by a picture in a book of children's stories depicting a huntsman's funeral procession followed by all the creatures of the forest. The movement begins with a familiar tune, the round *Bruder Martin* or *Frère Jacques*: for mock-pathetic effect the tune is put into the minor key and first played by a solo double bass high in its register. In this arrangement, the piano fills in some of the parts of the round, and also imitates the drums of the funeral procession.

Bamboo in the Breeze

Arranged by Edward Huws Jones

Trad. Chinese

Bamboo in the Breeze is an arrangement of a traditional Chinese melody, originally for the two-stringed fiddle called the *erhu*. Edward Huws Jones says that the melody would have been played unaccompanied, but he has added an atmospheric piano part which supports it with notes taken mostly from its five-note scale. He advises players to 'enjoy the give-and-take in the middle section as the piano and violin take it in turns to sing the melody'.

Castle on a Cloud

from Boublil & Schönberg's *Les Misérables*

B:3

Arranged by Alan Bullard

Music and lyrics by
Claude-Michel Schönberg (born 1944), Alain Boublil (born 1941),
Jean-Marc Natel (born 1942) and Herbert Kretzmer (born 1925)

Les Misérables is a highly successful musical, first performed in Paris in 1980, with a 'through-sung' score (without spoken dialogue). It is based on the well-known 19th-century French novel of the same name (meaning 'The Wretched') by Victor Hugo, which centres on the pursuit of an escaped prisoner, Jean Valjean, by the determined Inspector Javert. Another important character is Cosette, who is first encountered as an eight-year-old girl sent to live in a household where she is put to work and treated poorly. She sings a song, in an unusual mixture of 3/4, 2/4 and 4/4 time, in which she dreams of a 'castle on a cloud' where she will find friendship and an easier life.

C:1

The Ceilidh

No. 20 from *Fast Forward*

Katherine Colledge (born 1952)
and Hugh Colledge (born 1945)

Katherine and Hugh Colledge are a British wife-and-husband team responsible for many volumes of music for young string players – Katherine specialising in writing for strings and Hugh providing the piano accompaniments. They both worked as instrumental teachers in London before moving to Norfolk, in the east of England, in 1995. In this piece from their collection *Fast Forward*, they portray a 'ceilidh' (a Gaelic word, pronounced '*kay*-lee'), a sociable evening of Scottish or Irish dancing. The tune is a jig in traditional style, and the opening bars suggest the band tuning up.

Angry Tango

from *More Mood Swings*

Timothy Kraemer
(born 1947)

The British cellist Timothy Kraemer (also a professional photographer) has composed and arranged several collections for beginner string players. This piece, which originally comes from his children's opera *Good King Wenceslas*, is in the style of the Argentine national dance, the tango. He comments: 'When you watch two people dancing a tango they often look quite annoyed – even angry! Playing this tune with that in mind will give it the extra energy it needs.'

Where did you sleep last night little bird?

C:3

Hol háltál az éjjel cinegemadár?

No. 5 from *Tíz Könnyű Hegedű-Zongoradarab*

Arranged by Endre Szervánszky

Trad. Hungarian

Endre Szervánszky (1911–77) was a much-respected Hungarian composer; he wrote choral and orchestral music, and many pieces for various different ensembles. He also taught composition at the Budapest Academy of Music from 1949 until his death. In 1955, Szervánszky published *Tíz Könnyű Hegedű-Zongoradarab* (Ten Easy Pieces for violin and piano), all of them arrangements of Hungarian folk songs. The fifth piece is based on a tune in typically Hungarian short phrases, with an accompaniment suggesting the drone of the bagpipes.